The Bumper Book of
Instant Art
for
BIBLE CUT-OUTS

Lesley Jankowska

First published in 1995 in Great Britain by
KEVIN MAYHEW LTD
Rattlesden
Bury St Edmunds, Suffolk IP30 0SZ

Catalogue No 1396031
ISBN 0 86209 637 5

Cover by Roy Mitchell
Typesetting by Vicky Brown
Printed in Great Britain

Introduction

This book is a compilation of artwork for model-making projects, taken from the highly successful *Palm Tree Instant Art for Bible Cut-outs Books 1, 2 and 3*. These books have enjoyed a wide range of uses in Bible-based work with children in schools, Sunday schools, churches, clubs and homes. Such is the popularity of these earlier books, that we have decided to gather together the best of all the Bible cut-outs into one handy volume.

Given here are 24 models based on the Old Testament stories and 28 models based on stories from the New Testament. They range from simple one-page pieces, such as 'Joseph and the Coat of many colours', through to the five pages of artwork required for such pieces as 'The Birth of Jesus'. Some of the models have moving parts, others have stand-up backgrounds to complete the scene. With a little help these models will give pleasure to children who simply love colouring in, as well as being ideal for older children who enjoy craft activities.

• photocopying

The book's format allows it to be placed flat on the photocopier and the pages have been printed on one side only to give the best possible quality of reproduction. Most photocopiers will take a fine grade of card, and photocopying the models onto card, rather than gluing a paper copy on to card will give a better and quicker result. If the photocopier will make enlarged copies, you may wish to consider reproducing the drawings in a larger size than they are printed in the book.

• equipment required

scissors (use ones with rounded points)
sticky tape or glue
thin card or empty cereal packets
adhesive putty
  (to fix the bases of figures to surface)
colouring pencils, felt tips or paints
split pins
craft knife ONLY TO BE USED BY AN ADULT –
  for cutting slits if necessary. This can be
  done prior to the children's meeting.

• method

Either photocopy each page onto card, or glue the paper photocopy onto thin card or cereal packet

Colour in all the figures etc.

Cut around thick black outlines

Read instructions for cutting slots and fold-under bases

Position figures using adhesive putty if necessary to make more stable

Collect together all left-over scraps and tidy up!

• copyright

Material in this book is copyright-free, provided that it is used for the purposes for which it is intended. The usual copyright restrictions apply to any commercial use.

• user's responses

This series of 'instant art' books has been developed in response to ideas and suggestions from those who use the existing books. Any suggestions you might have for new titles would be warmly received and carefully considered!

Contents

Glue this page on to thin card or cereal packet and cut around outlines. Fold under bases and tape the support on to back of tree. Position Adam and Eve on either side of the tree slightly in front and hook serpent on top of tree near to Eve. Colour or paint before cutting out or when scene is complete.

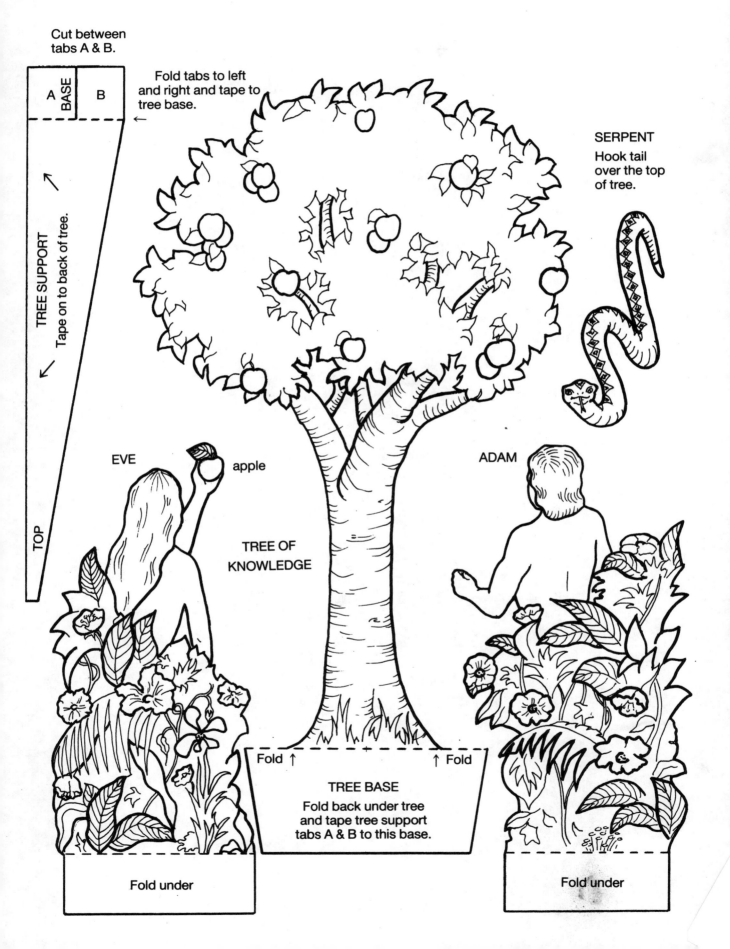

Cut between tabs A & B.

A BASE B

Fold tabs to left and right and tape to tree base.

TREE SUPPORT
Tape on to back of tree.

TOP

SERPENT
Hook tail over the top of tree.

EVE

apple

ADAM

TREE OF KNOWLEDGE

Fold ↑   ↑ Fold

TREE BASE
Fold back under tree and tape tree support tabs A & B to this base.

Fold under

Fold under

Glue page on to thin card or cereal packet and colour or paint. Cut around outlines and fold under base of each figure and stand them in and around the Ark.

RAINBOW

Keep this aside till Ark is made and tape on to far side of Ark behind deckhouse.

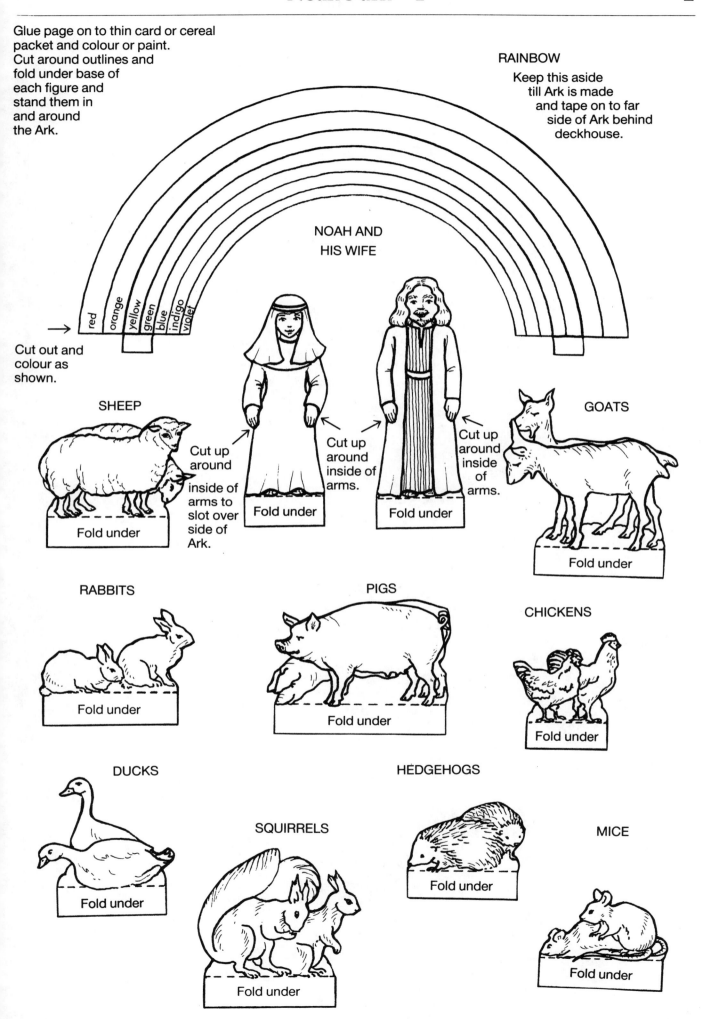

NOAH AND HIS WIFE

red orange yellow green blue indigo violet

Cut out and colour as shown.

SHEEP

Cut up around inside of arms to slot over side of Ark.

Fold under

Cut up around inside of arms.

Fold under

Cut up around inside of arms.

Fold under

GOATS

Fold under

RABBITS

Fold under

PIGS

Fold under

CHICKENS

Fold under

DUCKS

Fold under

SQUIRRELS

Fold under

HEDGEHOGS

Fold under

MICE

Fold under

Glue page on to card, colour and cut out animals. Fold under bases.
Position on and around Ark.

PARROTS

PENGUINS

LIONS

Cut up between
parrots tails
and slot on to Ark
or an animal's
back.

Fold under

Fold under

GIRAFFES

MONKEYS

ZEBRA

Fold under

Fold under

ELEPHANTS

RHINOS

Fold under

Fold under

Fold under

Place animals according to scale.
Elephants, giraffes and zebras will stand in Ark.

Glue page on to card and colour.
Cut out around outlines, cut
along slots and fold into position
and glue together.

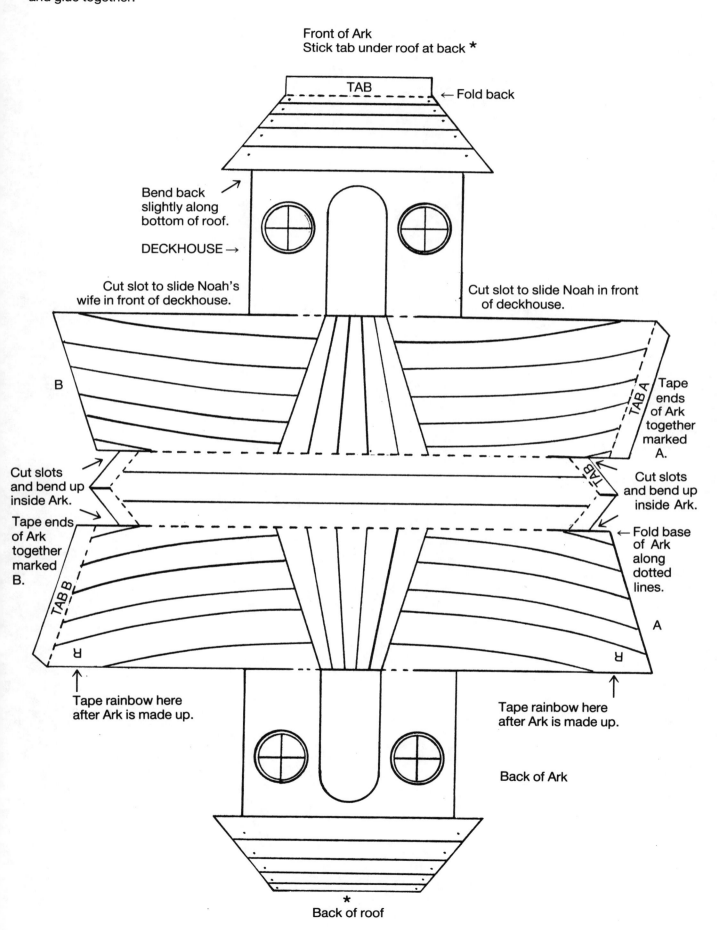

Front of Ark
Stick tab under roof at back *

TAB ← Fold back

Bend back
slightly along
bottom of roof.

DECKHOUSE →

Cut slot to slide Noah's
wife in front of deckhouse.

Cut slot to slide Noah in front
of deckhouse.

B

TAB A

Tape
ends
of Ark
together
marked
A.

TAB A

Cut slots
and bend up
inside Ark.

Cut slots
and bend up
inside Ark.

Tape ends
of Ark
together
marked
B.

TAB B

← Fold base
of Ark
along
dotted
lines.

A

Tape rainbow here
after Ark is made up.

Tape rainbow here
after Ark is made up.

Back of Ark

*
Back of roof

Genesis 11:1-9

Glue page on to thin card and colour. Cut around outlines and fold under the base of each figure. Set up a scene as shown on the cover. You could make a landscape, perhaps a tray of sand, to set the tower on. A backdrop of blue paper with clouds painted or stuck on will add to the effect.

BUILDING MATERIALS

Fold under

Fold under

BUILDERS

Fold under

Fold under

Glue all the parts of the tower on this page and the next on to thin card.
Colour and cut around the outlines. Take the base (5), make all its slots and
folds, and form it into a circle. Glue or tape the base. Fix parts 4, 3, 2 and 1
inside each other and on to the base, as shown in the finished picture.

FINISHED TOWER

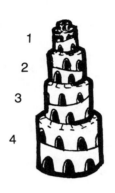

1 TOP

Bend into a circle and glue here.

Cut slits to the fold line.

Bend into a circle
and glue here.

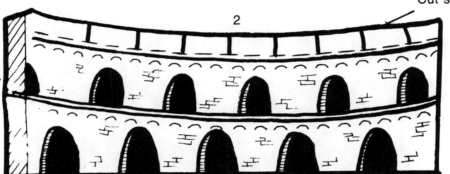

Fold inwards along
the dotted line.

Cut slits to the fold line.

Fold inwards along the dotted line.

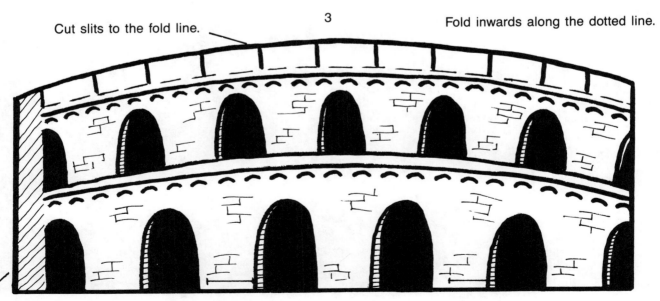

Bend into a circle
and glue here.

Cut slot

Cut slot

Follow the instructions on the previous page.

Bend into a circle and glue here.

Slot tabs on 4 into slots on 3.

4

Cut slits to the fold line.

Fold inwards along the dotted line.

Cut slot

Slot tabs on 5 into slots on 4.

5

Cut slot

TAB

BASE

Bend into a circle and glue here.

Genesis 24:15-21
Glue page on to thin card and colour. Cut around outlines and fold under the base of each figure. Set up a scene with the well in the background.

CAMELS AT THE WELL

REBECCA

Fold water forward
along the dotted line.

ABRAHAM'S SERVANT

Fold under

Fold under

Genesis 25: 27-34

Glue page on to thin card.
Colour and cut out.
Position Esau slightly
behind Jacob so that
Esau's hand is
under the bowl.

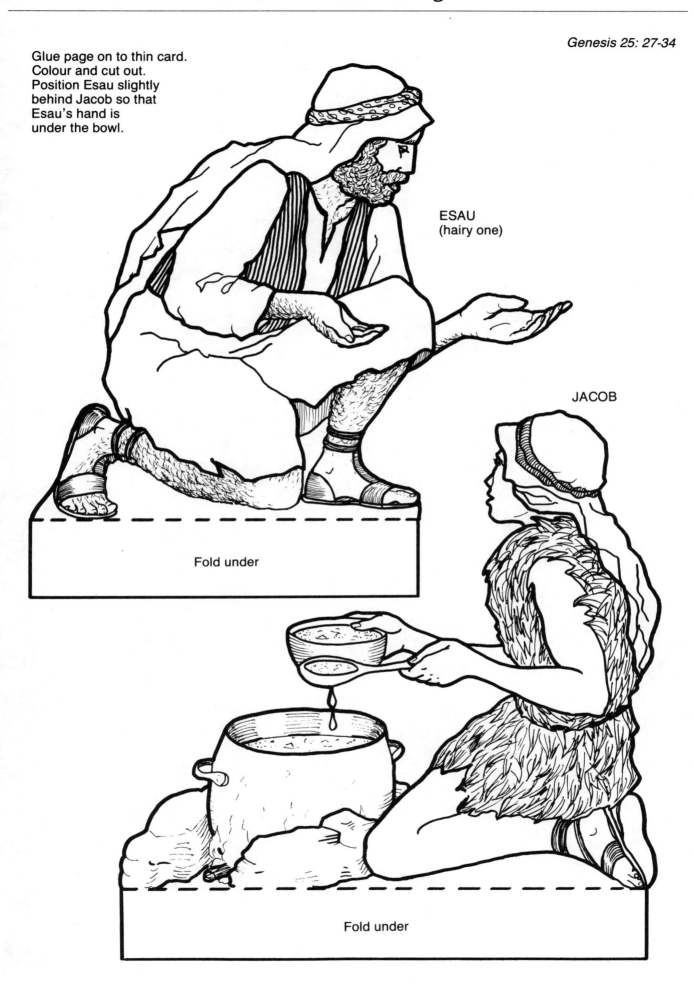

ESAU
(hairy one)

JACOB

Fold under

Fold under

Jacob's dream

Genesis 28:10-22

Glue page on to thin card and colour. Cut around outlines and fold under the base of each figure. Set up a scene. You could make a backdrop of dark blue paper painted as a starry night.

LADDER OF ANGELS

Fold under

JACOB

Fold under

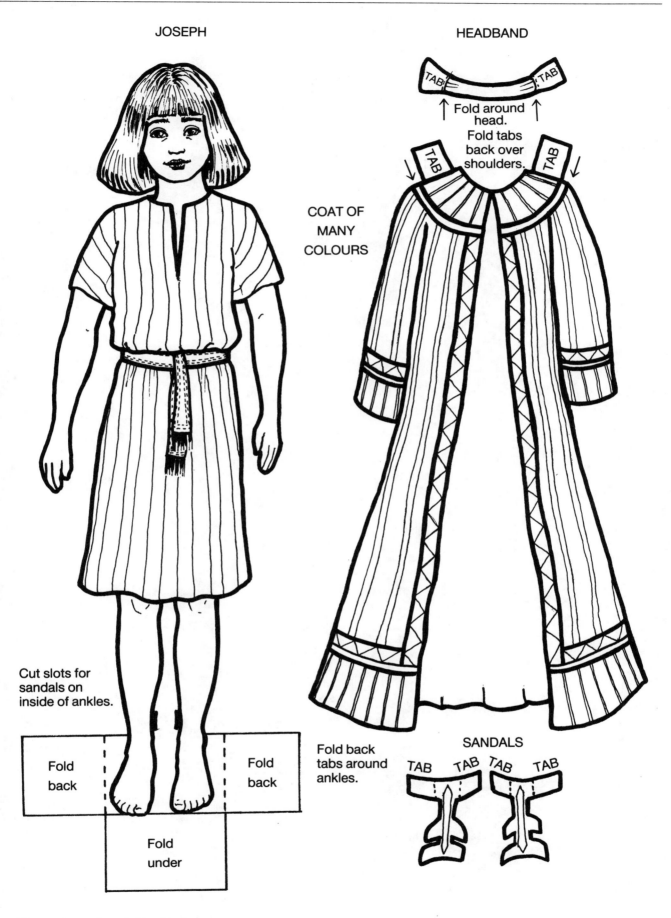

JOSEPH

HEADBAND

TAB   TAB

↑ Fold around ↑
head.
Fold tabs
back over
shoulders.

TAB   TAB

COAT OF
MANY
COLOURS

Cut slots for
sandals on
inside of ankles.

Fold
back

Fold
back

Fold
under

Fold back
tabs around
ankles.

SANDALS

TAB TAB TAB TAB

Glue page on to card and colour.
Cut out figure and dress in coat, sandals
and headband. If figure needs extra support,
copy the tree support on 'Adam and Eve' page
and tape to the back of the figure and to the base.

Cut out strip A before sticking page on to thin card. Colour and cut out all figures. Place river and bulrushes at front of scene, with baby basket behind bulrushes B. Place figures along back of riverbank. Pull strip A to float Moses in basket from behind the rushes towards the princess. Notice Miriam watching from behind the bulrushes.

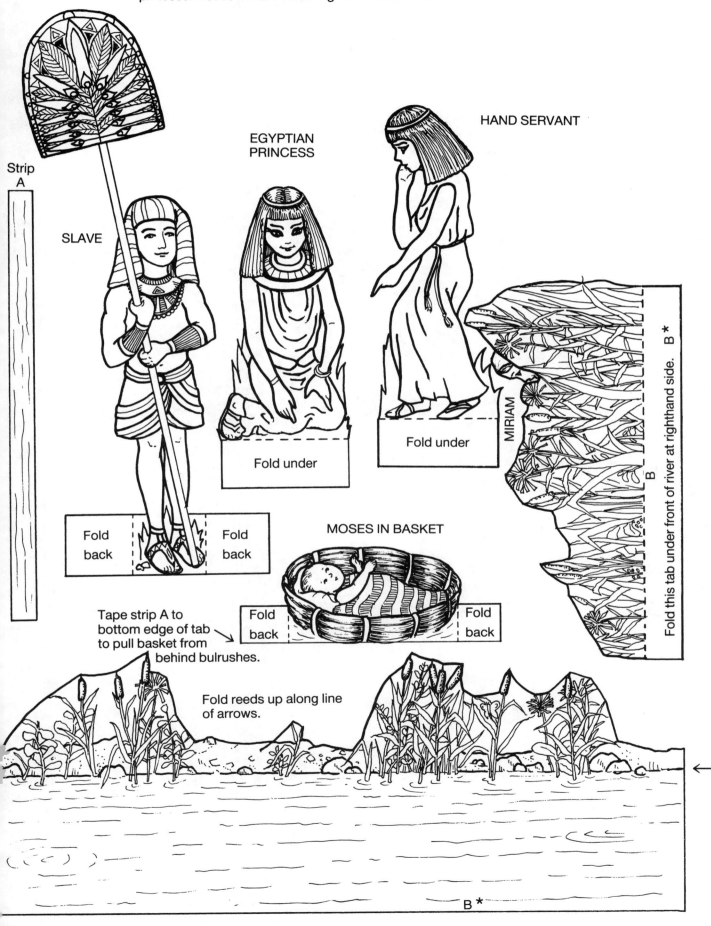

Strip
A

SLAVE

EGYPTIAN
PRINCESS

HAND SERVANT

Fold under

Fold under

MIRIAM

Fold this tab under front of river at righthand side.   B *

B

B

Fold
back

Fold
back

MOSES IN BASKET

Fold
back

Fold
back

Tape strip A to
bottom edge of tab
to pull basket from
behind bulrushes.

Fold reeds up along line
of arrows.

B *

Glue page on to card and colour.
Cut out around outlines and fold
bases under.

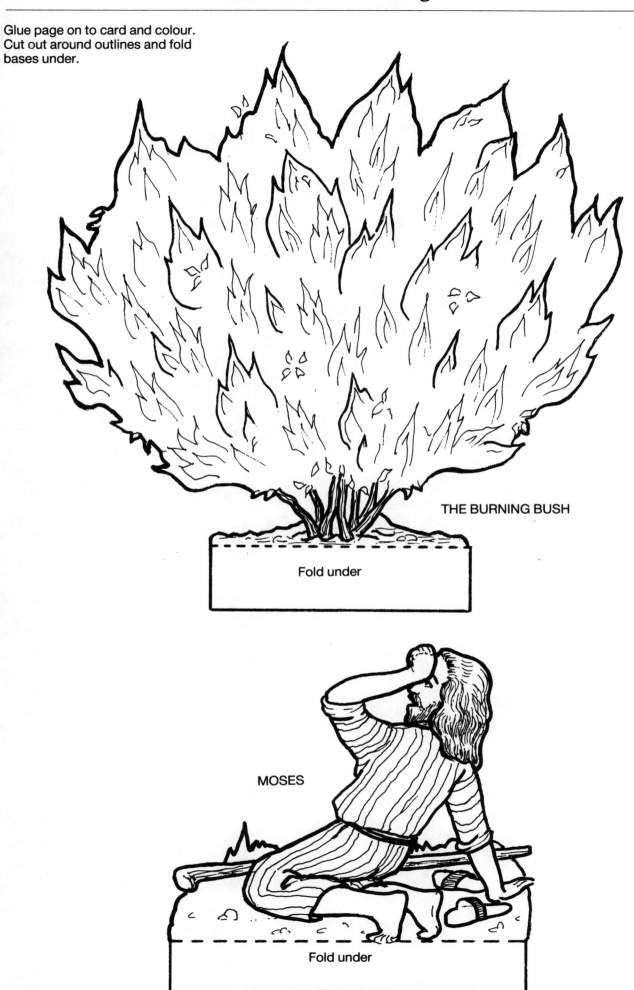

THE BURNING BUSH

Fold under

MOSES

Fold under

Glue page on to card and colour. Cut out all parts of scene and the Red Sea on the next page. Stand the Red Sea as shown below and tape to table or thick card to keep it stable. Slit the Red Sea in the middle.

Taking a pencil, roll the two free corners tightly around the pencil to make a giant wave effect.

MOSES

Set scene up as above.

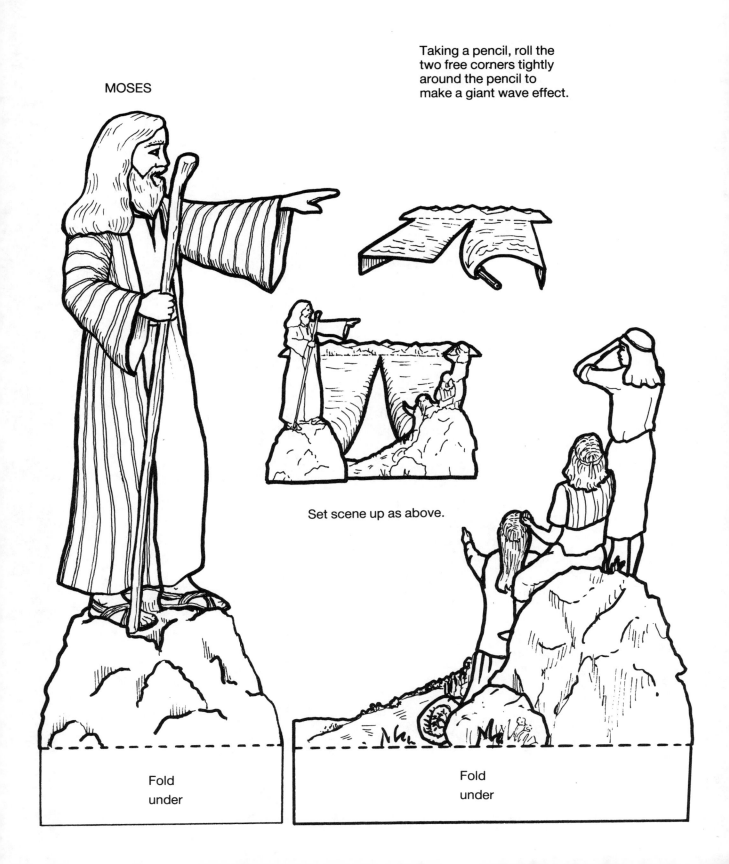

Fold under

Fold under

Glue page on to card and colour. Cut out and fold down side flaps and fold up mountains at back. Follow directions and diagrams on previous page.

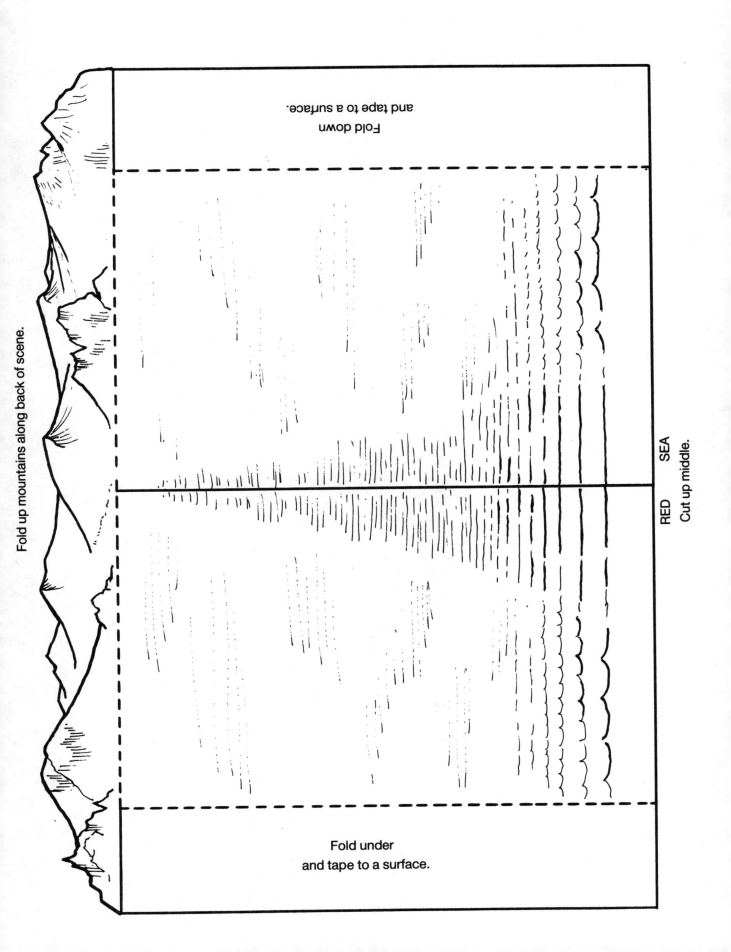

Exodus 17:1-7 and Numbers 20:1-13
Glue all the pieces with a heavy outline on to thin card and colour. Cut around the outlines. Using a split pin, join Moses' arm to his body so that the arm can be moved up and down. Cut out the hole to fit Moses' stick through his hand. Place the stick in his hand and tape it at the back. Continue with the next page.

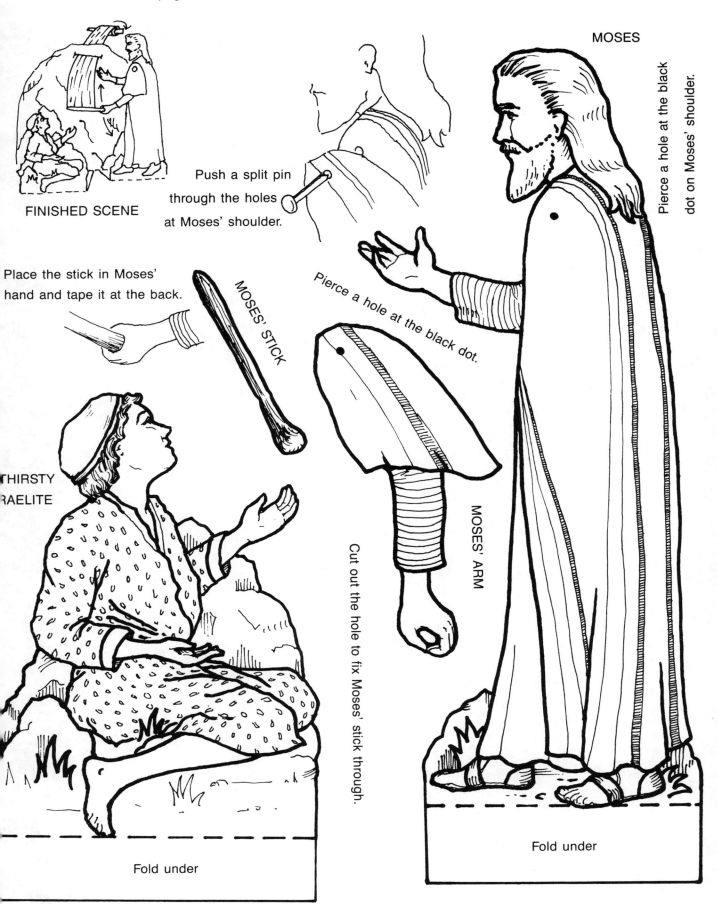

FINISHED SCENE

Push a split pin through the holes at Moses' shoulder.

Place the stick in Moses' hand and tape it at the back.

MOSES' STICK

Pierce a hole at the black dot.

Cut out the hole to fix Moses' stick through.

MOSES' ARM

THIRSTY ISRAELITE

MOSES

Pierce a hole at the black dot on Moses' shoulder.

Fold under

Fold under

The stream of water should be made using paper and the great rock should be made of card. Colour both pieces and cut them out. Fold under the base of the rock and cut the slot in the top. Roll the stream of water around a pencil and insert the top through the slot in the rock. Tape the rock to a firm base and position the figures in front. Moses' stick should be taped to the bottom of the stream of water poking through the slot. As you move his arm down the water will spout from the rock.

xtra support is needed for the rock, tape a couple
empty matchboxes to the back flap.

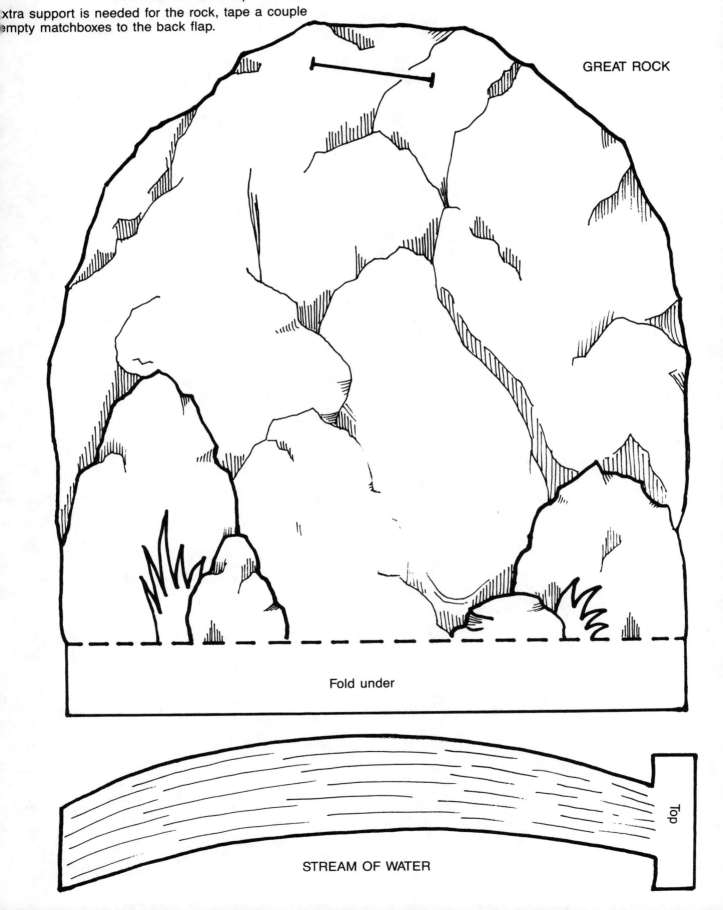

GREAT ROCK

Fold under

STREAM OF WATER

Top

Exodus 20:1-17 and Deuteronomy 5:1-22
Glue page on to thin card and colour. Cut out Moses and the two tablets. Cut the slots in Moses' cloak and insert the tablets. Bend Moses' hands on the fold lines to hold the tablets in place. Fold the sections marked to make Moses' base.

MOSES

Cut slot

Cut slot

TABLET

TABLET

Fold back

Fold back

Fold under

Exodus 25

Glue page on to thin card. Colour and cut out. Make folds along dotted lines and glue all corners and tabs.

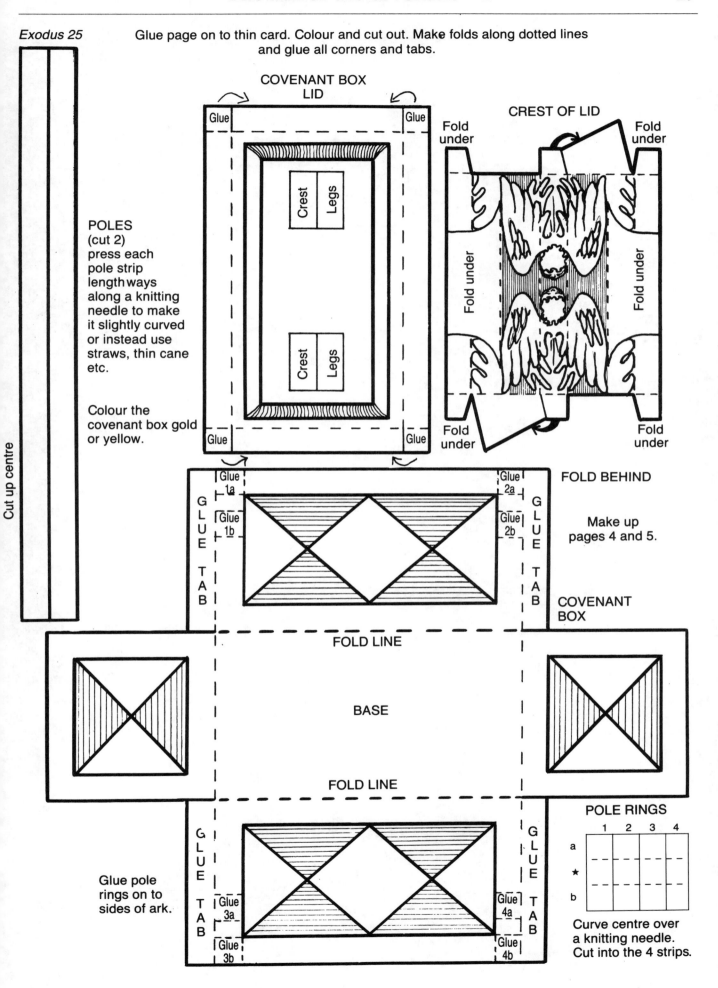

Cut up centre

COVENANT BOX
LID

Glue　　　Glue

Crest | Legs

Crest | Legs

Glue　　　Glue

POLES
(cut 2)
press each
pole strip
lengthways
along a knitting
needle to make
it slightly curved
or instead use
straws, thin cane
etc.

Colour the
covenant box gold
or yellow.

CREST OF LID

Fold
under　　　Fold
under

Fold under　　　Fold under

Fold
under　　　Fold
under

Glue
1a　　　Glue
2a

Glue
1b　　　Glue
2b

G
L
U
E

T
A
B

G
L
U
E

T
A
B

FOLD BEHIND

Make up
pages 4 and 5.

COVENANT
BOX

FOLD LINE

BASE

FOLD LINE

G
L
U
E

T
A
B

Glue
3a　　　Glue
4a

Glue
3b　　　Glue
4b

G
L
U
E

T
A
B

Glue pole
rings on to
sides of ark.

POLE RINGS

	1	2	3	4
a				
★				
b				

Curve centre over
a knitting needle.
Cut into the 4 strips.

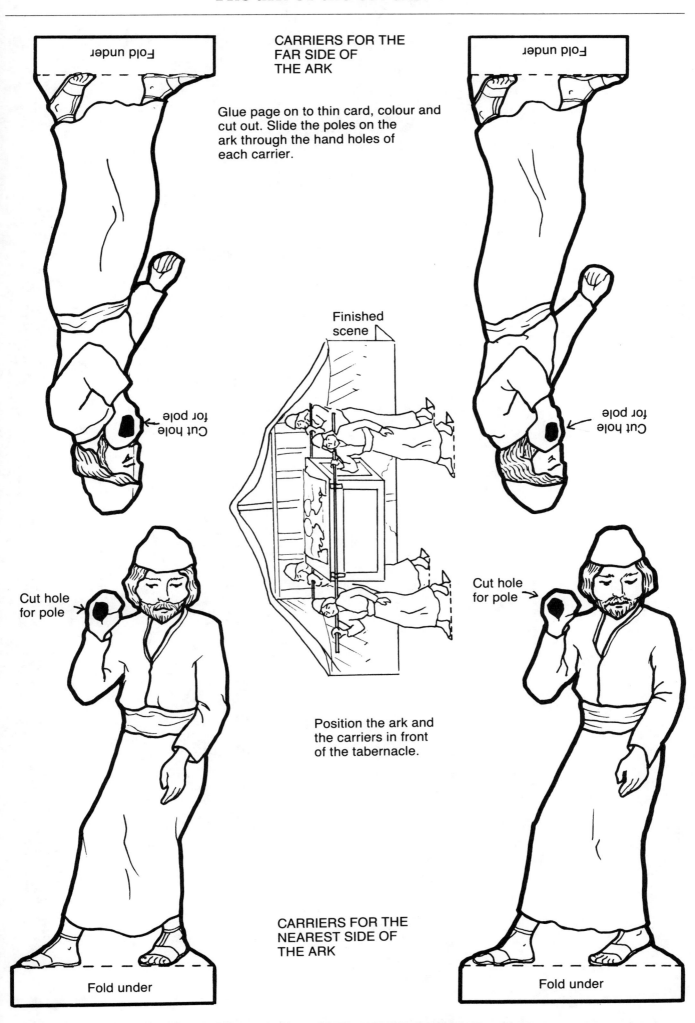

Fold under

Fold under

CARRIERS FOR THE
FAR SIDE OF
THE ARK

Glue page on to thin card, colour and
cut out. Slide the poles on the
ark through the hand holes of
each carrier.

Finished
scene

Cut hole
for pole

Cut hole
for pole

Cut hole
for pole

Cut hole
for pole

Position the ark and
the carriers in front
of the tabernacle.

CARRIERS FOR THE
NEAREST SIDE OF
THE ARK

Fold under

Fold under

THE TABERNACLE

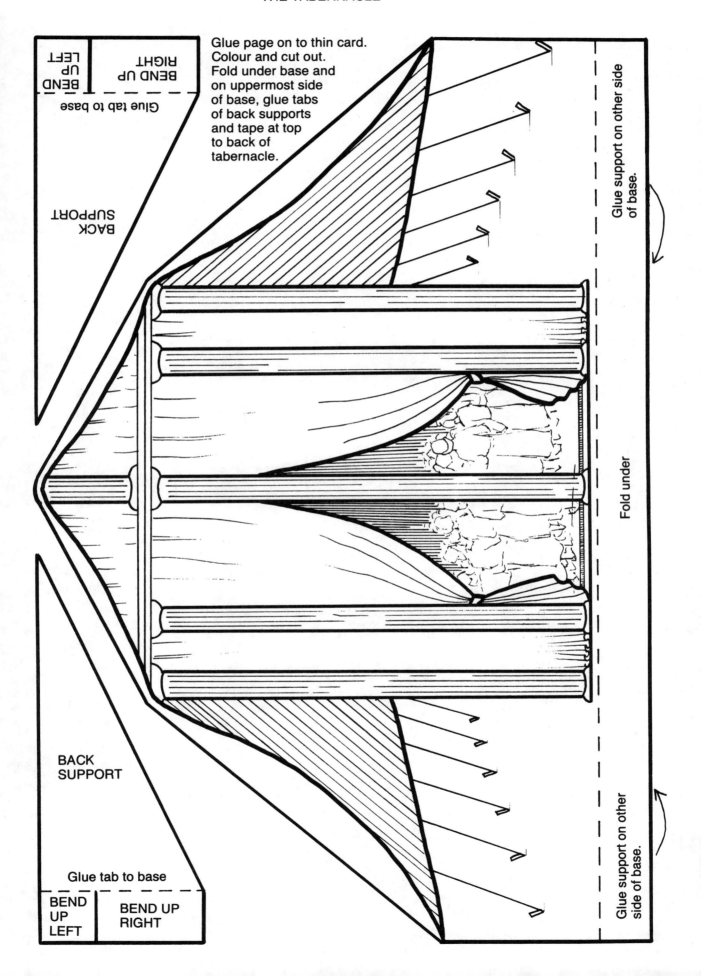

Glue page on to thin card. Colour and cut out. Fold under base and on uppermost side of base, glue tabs of back supports and tape at top to back of tabernacle.

BEND UP LEFT

BEND UP RIGHT

Glue tab to base

BACK SUPPORT

Glue support on other side of base.

Fold under

BACK SUPPORT

Glue tab to base

BEND UP LEFT

BEND UP RIGHT

Glue support on other side of base.

Joshua 4

Glue page on to thin card.
Colour and cut out.
Make up page 9.

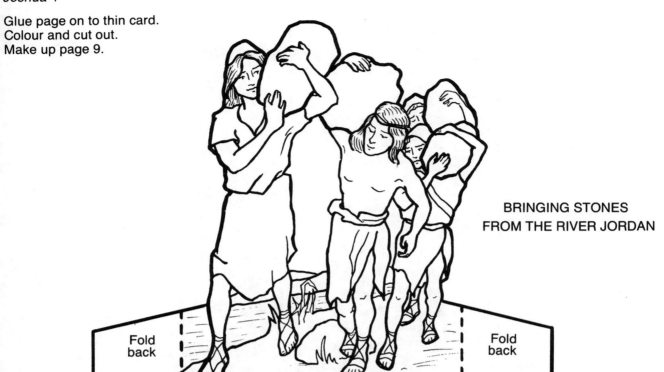

BRINGING STONES
FROM THE RIVER JORDAN

Fold
back

Fold
back

Fold under

Fold under

Fold under

Glue page on to thin card.
Colour and cut out.
Using figures from page 8,
set up scene .

JOSHUA

BUILDING
THE
MONUMENT

Fold under

Fold under

Joshua 6

Glue all the pieces with a heavy outline on this page and the next two pages on to thin card. Colour and cut out the figures and the walls of Jericho. Assemble Jericho as illustrated with the seven priests blowing trumpets and the soldiers shouting. Make a tube with thin card and, as the priests blow and the soldiers shout, blow the walls of the city down.

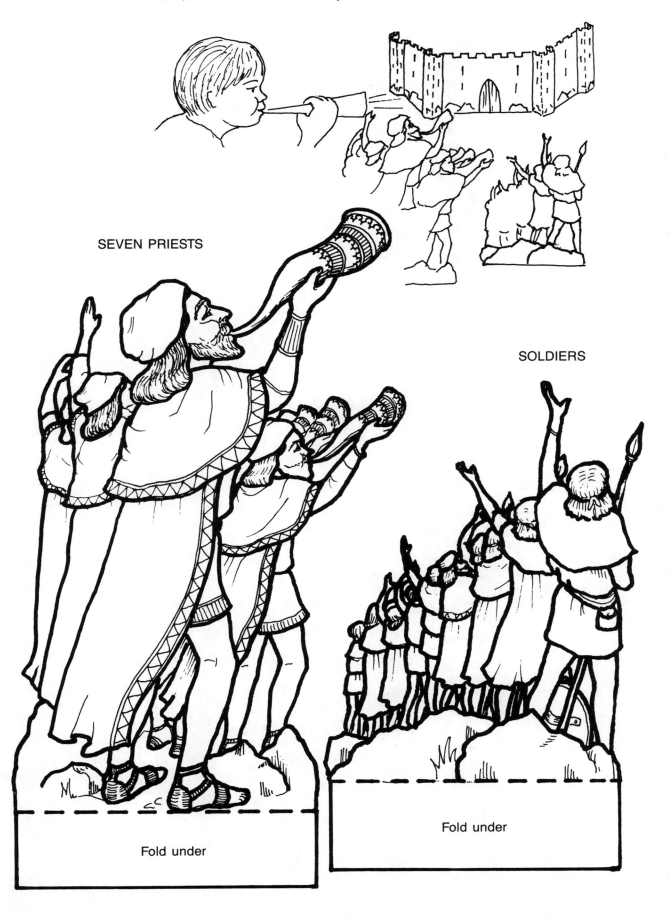

SEVEN PRIESTS

SOLDIERS

Fold under

Fold under

Fold along dotted lines.   Fold along dotted lines.

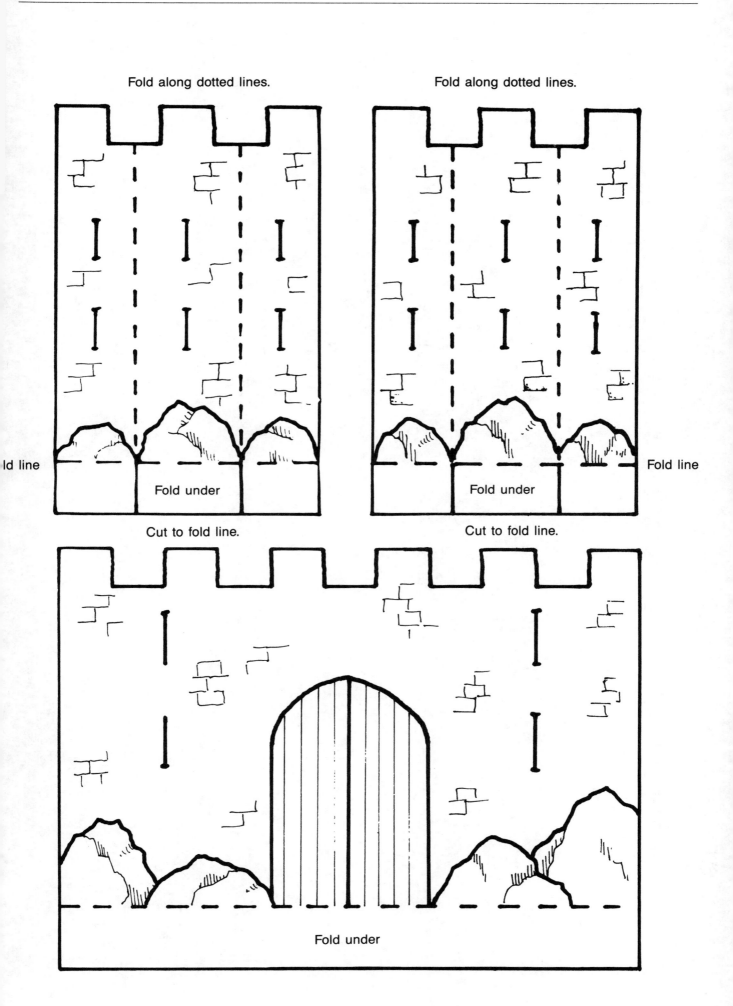

Id line   Fold line

Fold under   Fold under

Cut to fold line.   Cut to fold line.

Fold under

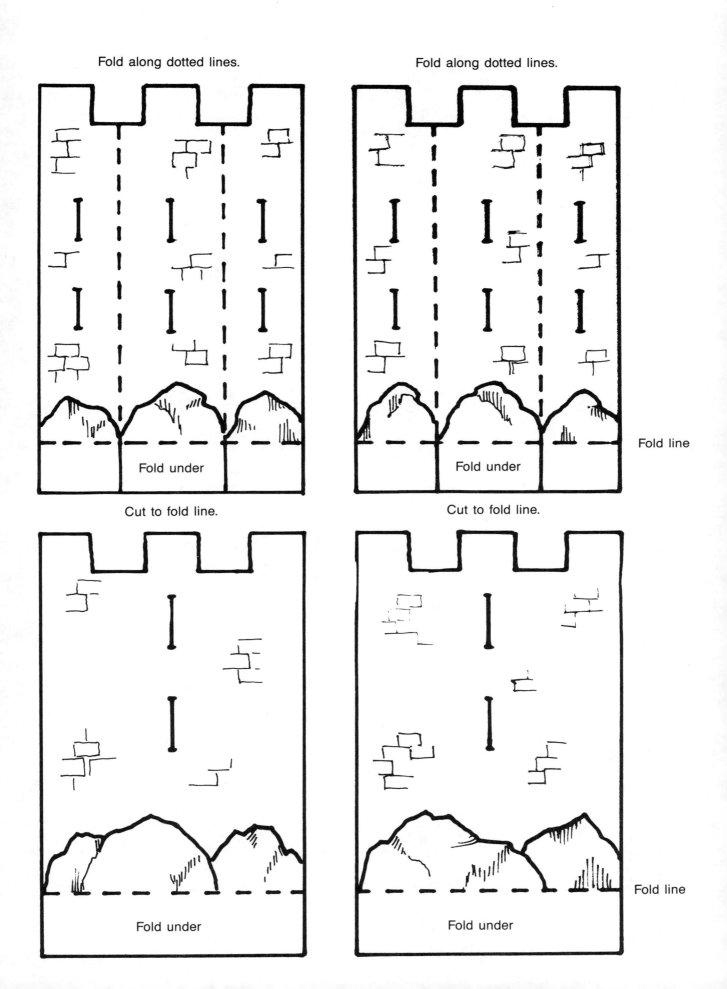

Fold along dotted lines.

Fold along dotted lines.

Fold under

Fold under

Fold line

Cut to fold line.

Cut to fold line.

Fold under

Fold under

Fold line

1 Samuel 3
Glue page on to thin card and colour. Cut around outlines. Position Samuel in front of the curtains and Eli in the foreground of the scene.

Fold back

Fold back

Fold back

Fold under

Fold under

Fold under

Fold back

Fold back

ELI

SAMUEL

Fold under

1 Samuel 16
Glue page on to thin card and colour. Cut out the figures and position them, Samuel holding the horn of oil over David's head.

HORN OF OIL

SAMUEL

BOY DAVID

Fold under

Fold under

1 Samuel 16

Glue page on to thin
card. Colour and
cut out. Fix split pin through David's
arms, Cut slit up David's leg.
Position David just
behind Saul's foot.
With needle and thread string
harp through holes and slot harp
between David's legs and arms.

DAVID

SAUL

TAB

Slot tab into slit
cut here

Fold under

Fold under

Glue page on to card and colour. Cut out figures and position with Philistine army in background.

GOLIATH

PHILISTINE ARMY

Fold under

Fold under

DAVID

Fold under

2 Samuel 18

Glue page on to thin card.
Colour and cut out.
Go on to page 12.

ABSOLEM

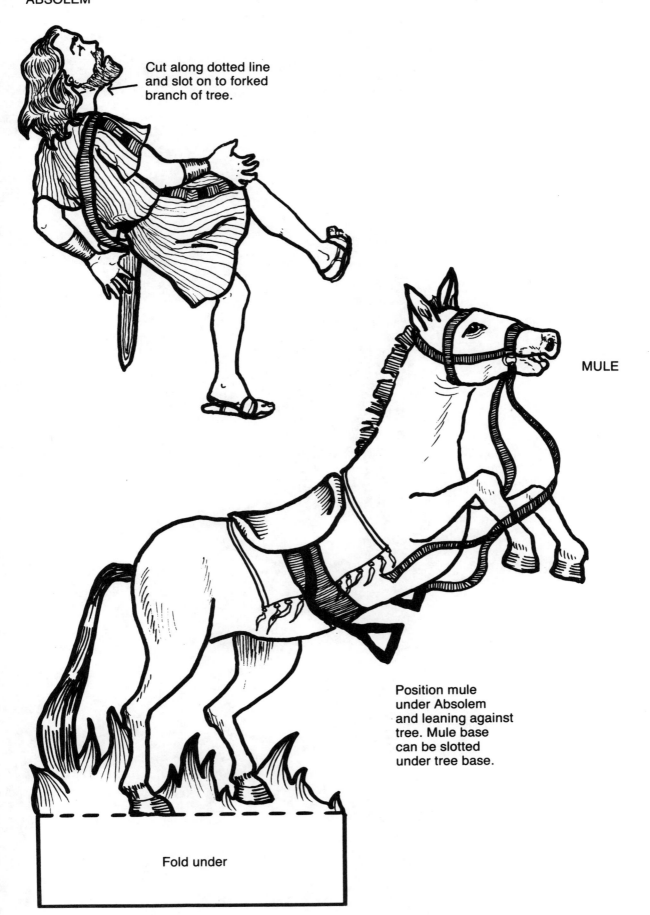

Cut along dotted line
and slot on to forked
branch of tree.

MULE

Position mule
under Absolem
and leaning against
tree. Mule base
can be slotted
under tree base.

Fold under

Glue page on to thin card.
Colour and cut out.
Fix back support behind
tree.

Set up scene
as below.

BACK
SUPPORT

FOLD
LEFT

FOLD
RIGHT

Fold under

1 Kings 3

Glue page on to thin card. Colour and cut out. Complete page 14.

SOLOMON

Cut slit

Fold under

Glue page on to thin card. Colour and cut out.
Slot baby into step. Arrange two mothers to the right of
Solomon.

Fold

Fold under

MOTHERS

Fold under

Daniel 5

Glue page on to thin card. Colour and cut out. Make up page 16.

Writing strips

FOLD	FOLD
1	2

Fold under

Glue page on to thin card. Colour and
cut out. Cut slits in wall and slide
2 strips of writing through slits.
Bend over ends.
Stick hand on to second
strip at end of writing*.
Hold hand and move
writing between slits.
Make back supports
for wall if necessary.

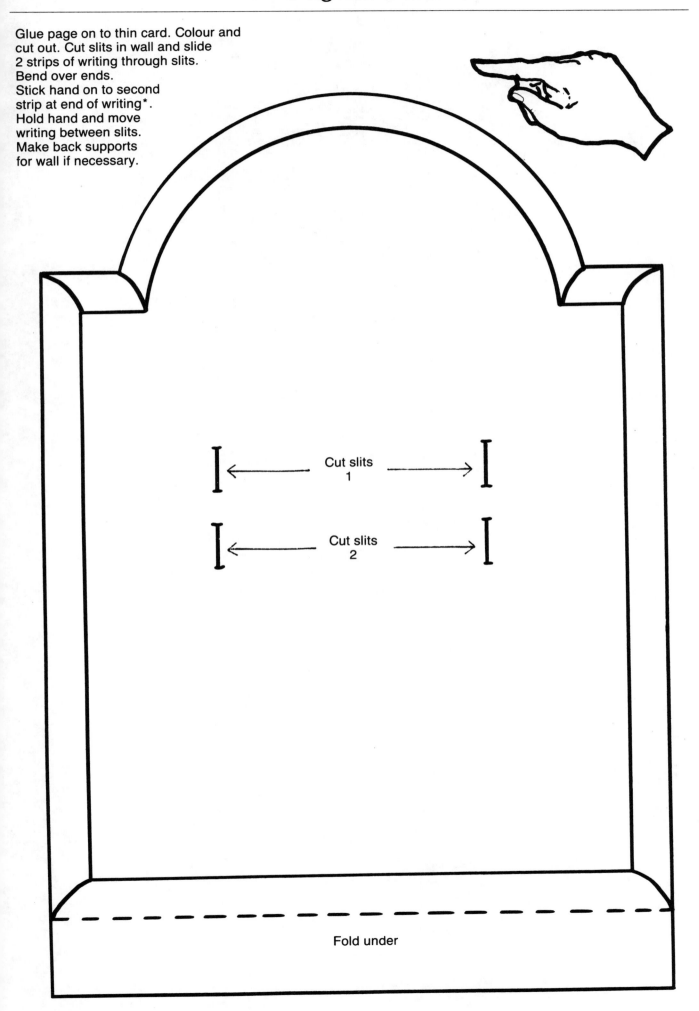

Cut slits
1

Cut slits
2

Fold under

Glue page on to card and colour. Cut out figures and fold bases under. Cut out lions' den and tape tabs under and bend into cave shape.

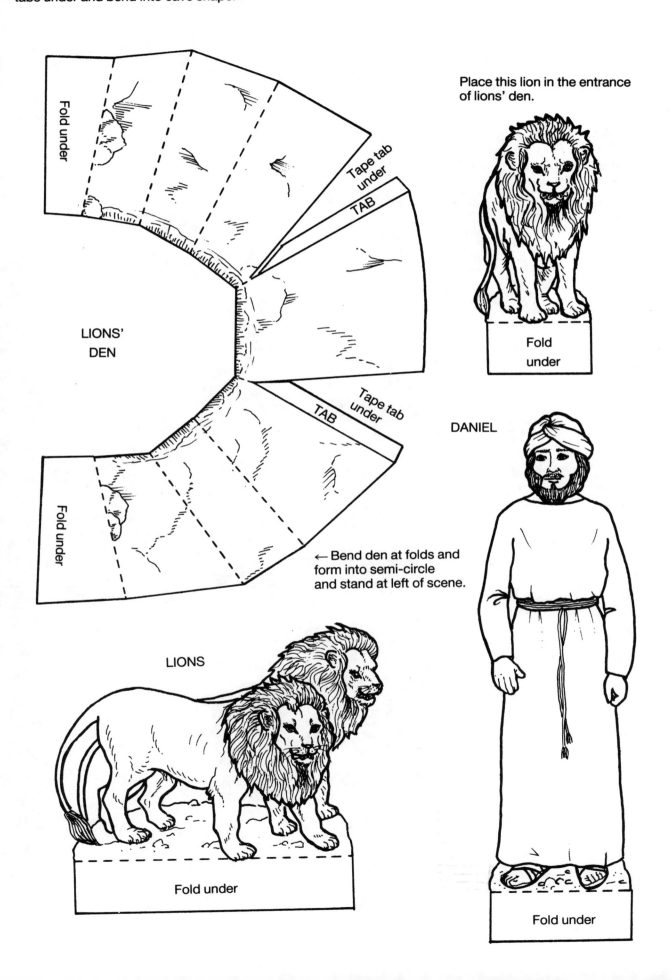

Place this lion in the entrance of lions' den.

Fold under

Fold under

LIONS' DEN

Tape tab under

TAB

Tape tab under

TAB

Fold under

Fold under

← Bend den at folds and form into semi-circle and stand at left of scene.

DANIEL

LIONS

Fold under

Fold under

Glue page on to thin card and colour. Cut out all pieces and assemble fish, slotting and taping all fins. Then tape up underneath of fish. Assemble Jonah and slide him feet first into fish's mouth. Make sea and beach of Nineveh on following page and swim the big fish across the sea.

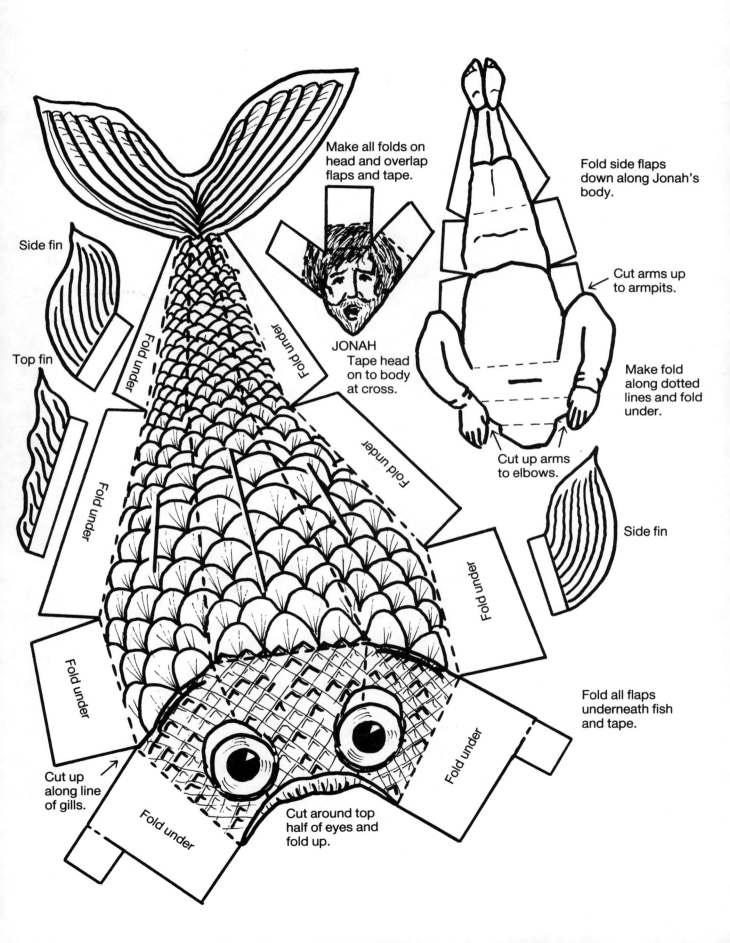

Make all folds on head and overlap flaps and tape.

Fold side flaps down along Jonah's body.

Side fin

Cut arms up to armpits.

Top fin

JONAH
Tape head on to body at cross.

Fold under

Fold under

Fold under

Make fold along dotted lines and fold under.

Fold under

Cut up arms to elbows.

Side fin

Fold under

Fold all flaps underneath fish and tape.

Fold under

Cut up along line of gills.

Fold under

Cut around top half of eyes and fold up.

Glue this page on to thin card and colour in the waves of the sea and the beach of Nineveh. Swim your fish carrying Jonah through the sea and deposit Jonah on the beach of Nineveh.

NINEVEH

Glue on to card, colour and cut out. Position the figures so that
the Angel Gabriel is telling Mary she will have a son.

ANGEL GABRIEL

Fold under

MARY

Fold under

Colour this page showing the star over Bethlehem and pin up behind your stable and nativity scene.

Glue page on to thin card. Cut out and colour.
Arrange into a scene. Make and decorate with straw a
small cardboard box to be a stable.

JOSEPH

MARY

BABY   JESUS

Fold under

Fold under

Fold under

LAMB

OX

Fold under

Fold under

Glue page on to thin card.
Cut out and colour.

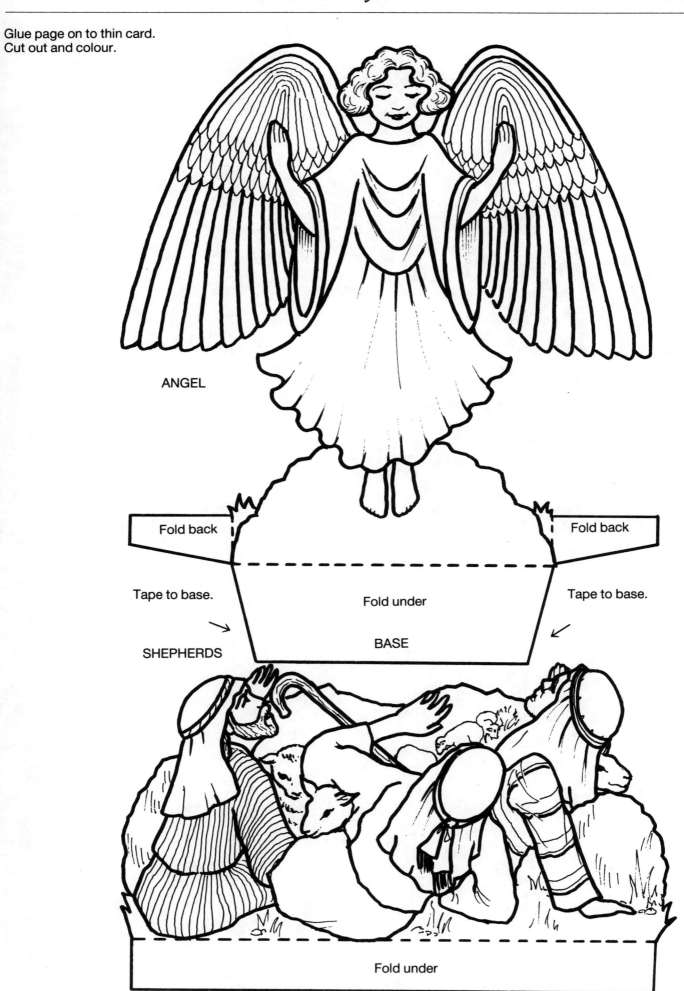

ANGEL

Fold back

Fold back

Tape to base.

Fold under

Tape to base.

SHEPHERDS

BASE

Fold under

Glue this page on to card.
Cut out and colour.
Place the Wise Men and the donkey
with the other
figures around
the nativity
scene.

THE WISE
MEN

Fold back

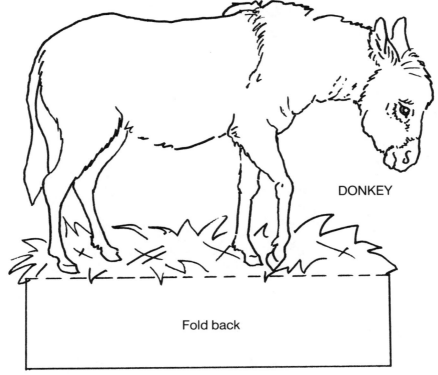

DONKEY

Fold back

Matthew 1:13-15
Glue page on to thin card and colour. Cut out the figures. Make a background scene if you like of desert and hills.

MARY AND JESUS

JOSEPH

Fold under

Fold under

Jesus in his father's workshop

Joseph was a carpenter. As an obedient child (Luke 2:51) Jesus would have helped in his father's workshop.

Glue page on to thin card and colour. Cut around outlines and set up a scene with the boy Jesus in front of the workbench.

JESUS

Fold back

Fold back

WORKBENCH

Fold under

Luke 2:41-52

Glue page on to thin card.
Colour and cut out.
Complete page 18 and
set up as finished scene.

Finished scene

TEMPLE
ELDERS

JESUS

Fold under

Fold under

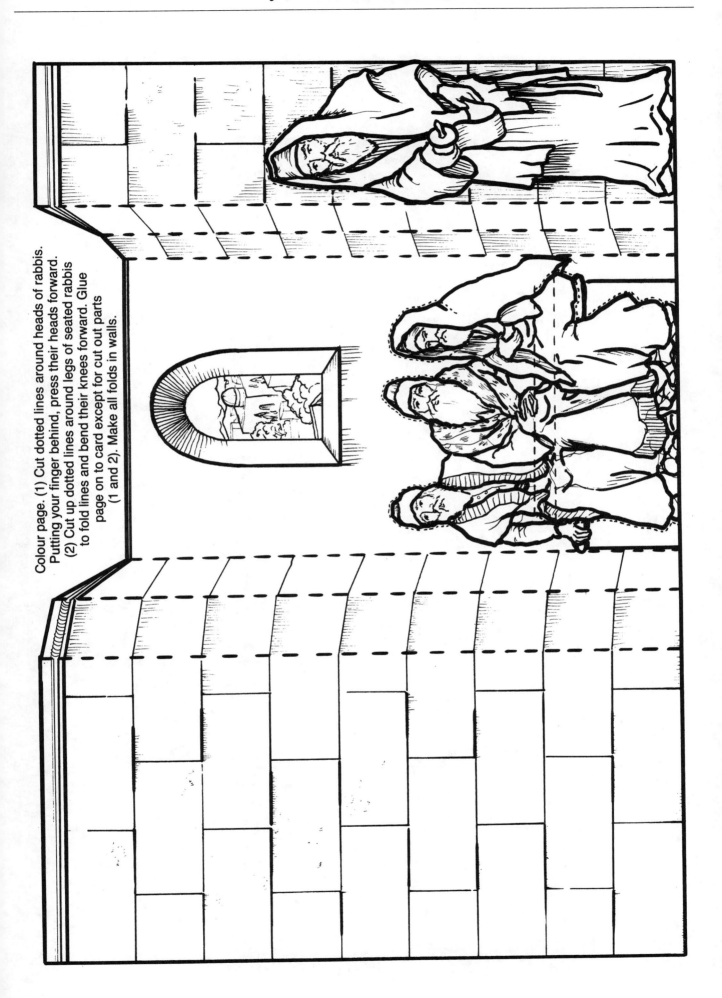

Colour page. (1) Cut dotted lines around heads of rabbis. Putting your finger behind, press their heads forward. (2) Cut up dotted lines around legs of seated rabbis to fold lines and bend their knees forward. Glue page on to card except for cut out parts (1 and 2). Make all folds in walls.

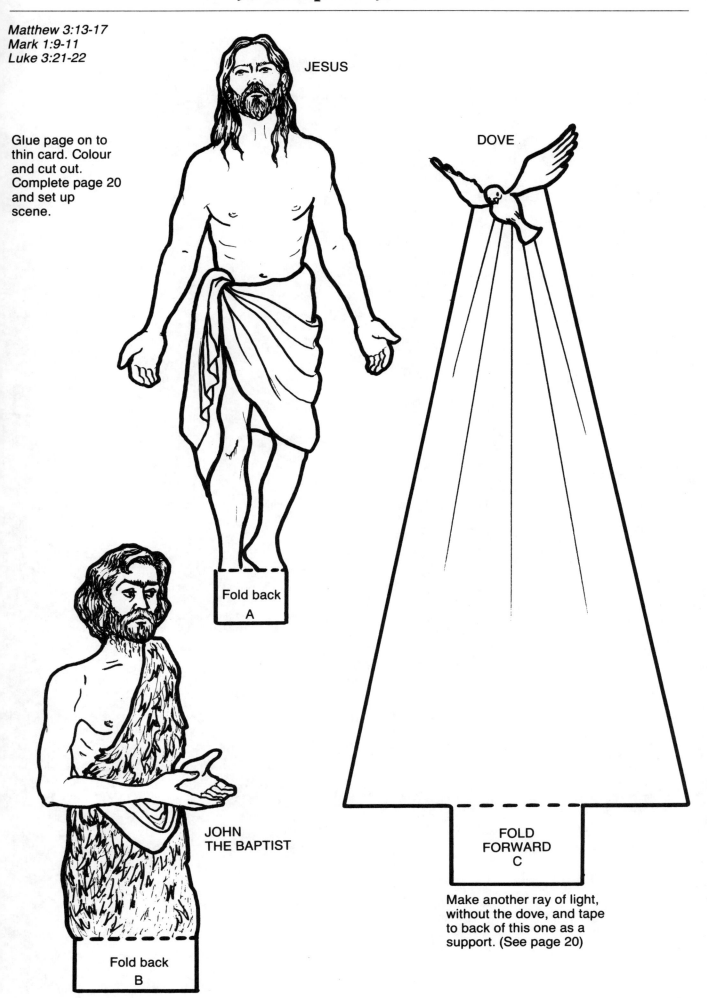

Matthew 3:13-17
Mark 1:9-11
Luke 3:21-22

Glue page on to
thin card. Colour
and cut out.
Complete page 20
and set up
scene.

JESUS

DOVE

Fold back
A

JOHN
THE BAPTIST

Fold back
B

FOLD
FORWARD
C

Make another ray of light,
without the dove, and tape
to back of this one as a
support. (See page 20)

Glue page on to thin card.
Cut out and colour. Fold up far bank and make
back support if necessary. Put tabs of
figures and ray of light in their
matching slots in river. Cut around
reeds of near bank (not cutting fold
lines at edges.) Make folds so that
reeds stand up as in
finished scene.

Finished
scene

RIVER
JORDAN

Glue this page on to thin card. Cut out and colour.
Arrange scene with the people at the wedding and
Jesus in background and the servant pouring wine in foreground.

THE BRIDE AND GROOM AND
GUESTS AT THE WEDDING

Fold back

Glue this page on to thin card. Cut out and colour.
Using a split pin fix arms through body of the servant
pouring from jug.

BACK
ARM

SERVANT
POURING WINE

JESUS

Fold
back

Fold back

Glue page on to thin card and cut out and colour.

JESUS

BOY WHO GIVES
LOAVES AND FISH

Fold back

Fold back

BASKET

LOAVES

FISH

Glue page on to thin card. Cut out and colour.
Position behind figures from previous page.

THE CROWD OF 5000

Fold under

Matthew 8:5-13
Luke 7:1-10

Glue page on to thin card.
Colour and cut out.
The Centurion's cloak is red.

Postion centurion
behind the servant's bed.

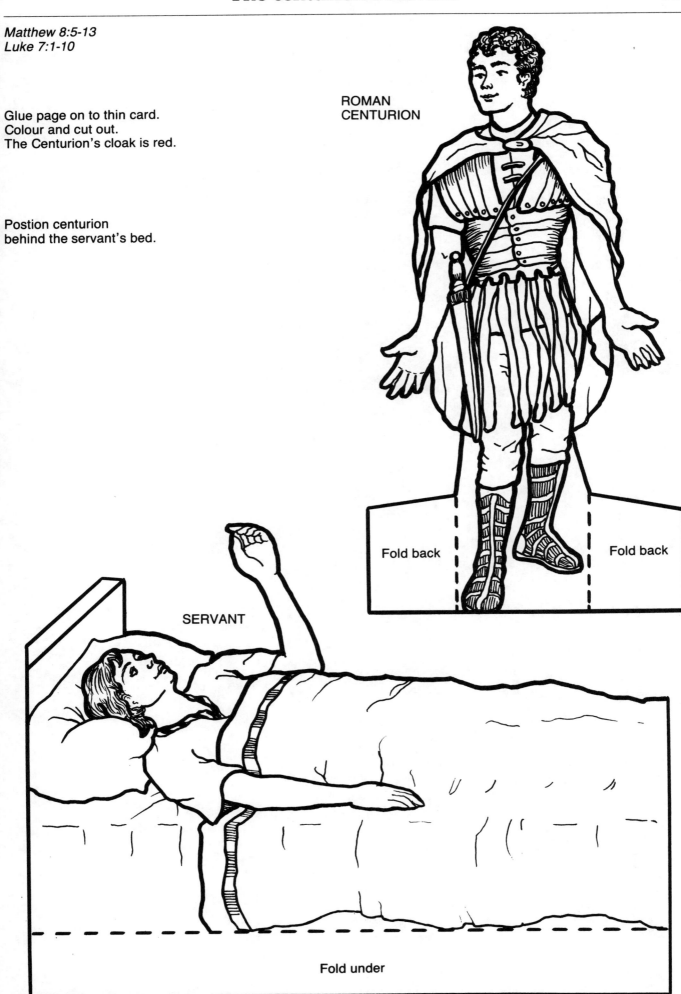

ROMAN
CENTURION

Fold back   Fold back

SERVANT

Fold under

Jesus heals a paralysed man – 1

Matthew 9:1-8
Mark 2:1-12
Luke 5:17-26

Glue page on to thin card.
Colour and cut out.
Cut slits in mattress.
Make folds in hands of
men on roof and fold through
slits in mattress. Slot tab
at head of sick man
through slit in mattress.

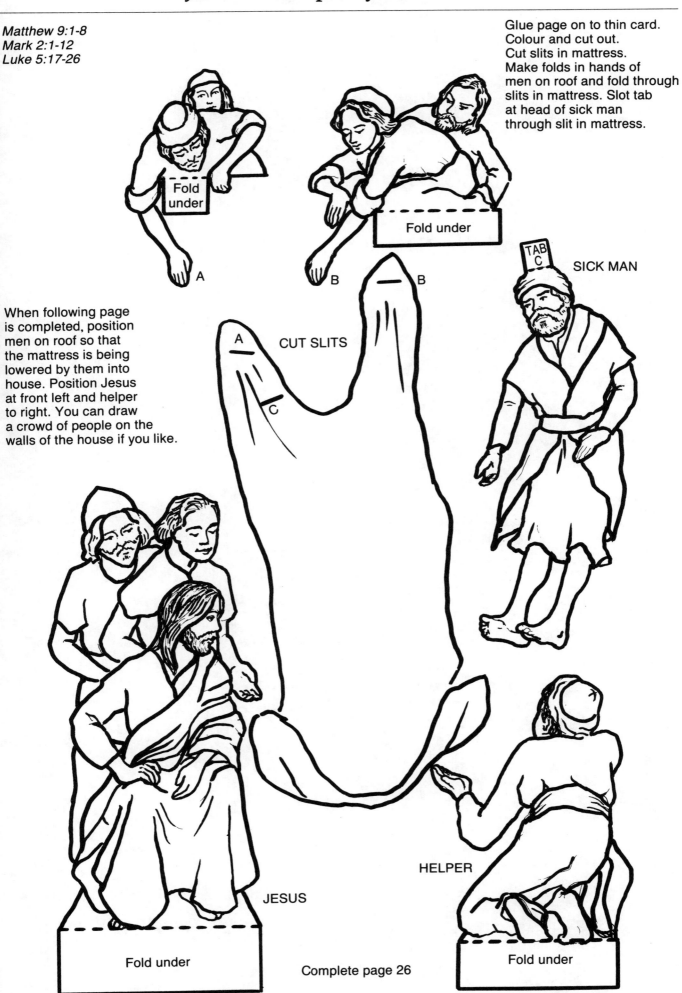

Fold under

Fold under

SICK MAN

CUT SLITS

When following page
is completed, position
men on roof so that
the mattress is being
lowered by them into
house. Position Jesus
at front left and helper
to right. You can draw
a crowd of people on the
walls of the house if you like.

JESUS

HELPER

Fold under

Complete page 26

Fold under

Glue page on to thin card. Colour and cut out. Fold and glue.

BUILDING

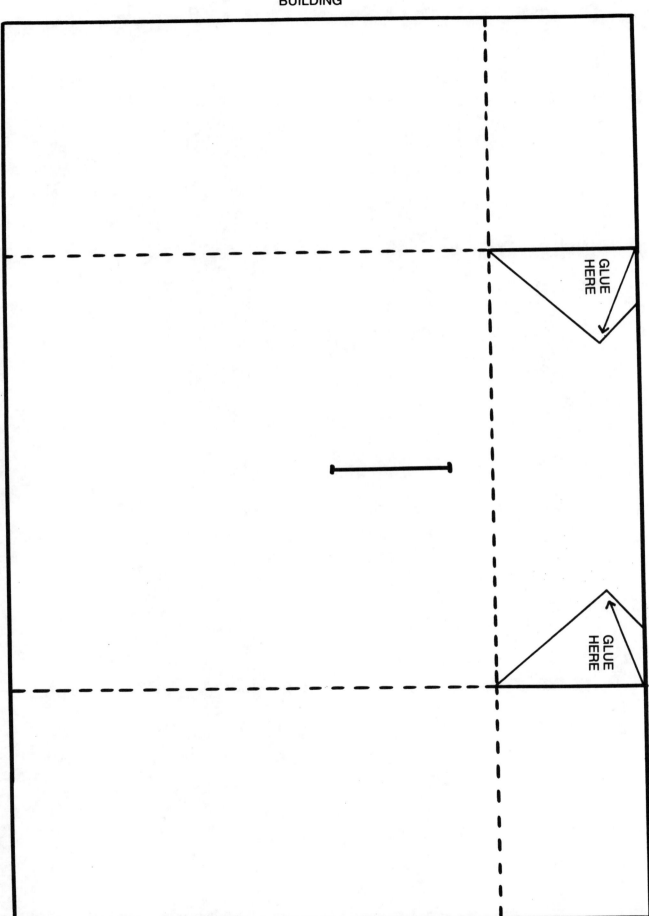

Matthew 13:1-9; Mark 4:1-9 and Luke 8:4-8
Glue page on to thin card and colour. Cut around outlines and arrange the pieces into a scene.

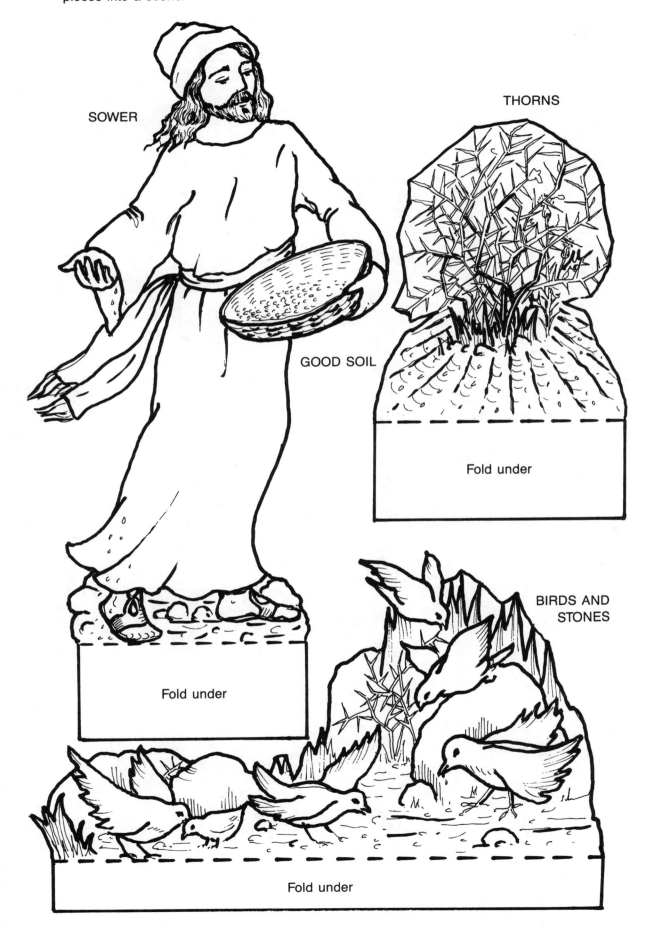

SOWER

THORNS

GOOD SOIL

Fold under

Fold under

BIRDS AND STONES

Fold under

Matthew 9:18-26
Mark 5:21-43
Luke 8:40-56

JAIRUS' DAUGHTER

BED

GLUE UNDER

GLUE UNDER

GLUE UNDER

GLUE UNDER

Fold under

Glue page on to thin card. Colour and cut out. Make folds and position bed with Jairus' daughter lying on it. Position Jesus at the foot of the bed healing her. Jairus' daughter stands up. Her father at the head of the bed raises his arms in joy.

JESUS

JAIRUS

Fold back

Fold back

Fold under

Glue page on to thin card. Cut out and colour.
Arrange robbers leaning over beaten man.

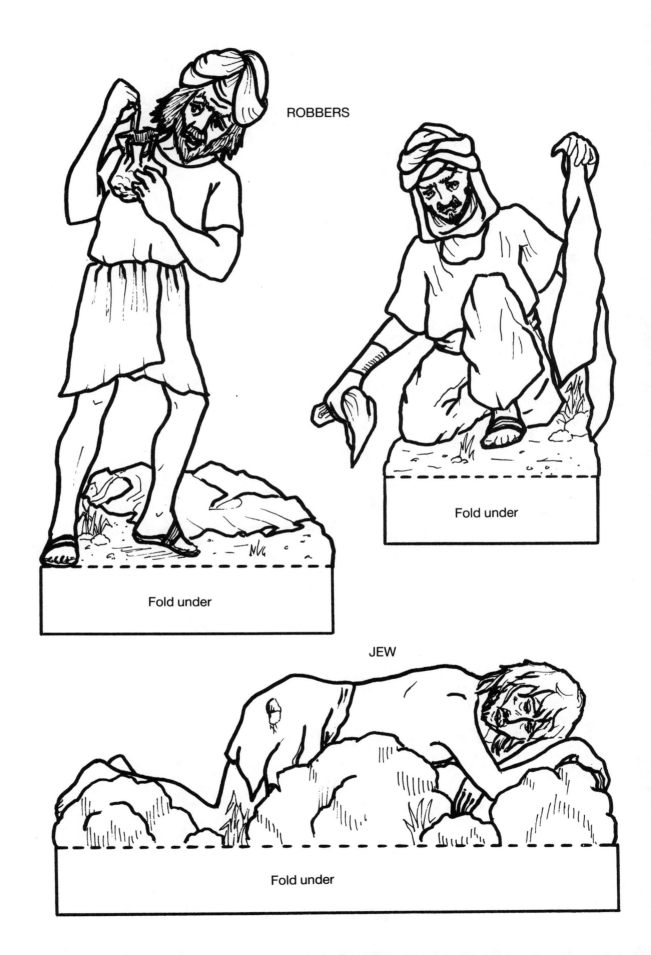

ROBBERS

Fold under

Fold under

JEW

Fold under

Glue page on to thin card.
Cut out and colour. Move
the figures as you go through
the story.

PRIEST

LEVITE

Fold under

SAMARITAN

Place Samaritan
leaning over
beaten man.

Cut up line
of arm marked
with arrow and
place over Jew's
head.

Fold under

Fold under

Luke 15:11-32
Glue page on to thin card and colour. Cut around outlines.

THE FATHER

THE PRODIGAL SON

Fold under

Fold under

Matthew 14:22-33; Mark 6:45-52 and John 6:16-21
Glue page on to thin card and colour. Cut out the two figures. Complete the next page.

JESUS

COMPLETED SCENE

PETER

Fold under

Fold under

Stick bases of the figures on to the lake (next page).

Glue page on to thin card and colour. Cut out around the clouds. Cut out the boat and fold it up along the dotted line. Fold up the shore along the dotted line. Set up the scene as shown on the previous page.

Stick Jesus' base here.

Stick Peter's base here.

LAKE

Glue this page on to thin card.
Cut out and colour. Set scene up
with the ten lepers at the back and
Jesus in the foreground to the right.

JESUS

Fold back

TEN
LEPERS

Fold back

Fold back

Matthew 19:13-15; Mark 10:13-16 and Luke 18:15-17
Glue page on to thin card and colour. Cut around outlines. Cut slots and place a child on each knee of Jesus.

Cut slot.

Cut along dotted lines
around hands.

Fold under

Fold under

Fold
back

Fold back

Fold under

John 9
Glue page on to thin card and colour. Cut around outlines.

JESUS

THE BLIND MAN

Fold under

Fold under

The good shepherd

68

John 10:7-18

Glue page on to thin card and colour. Cut around outlines. Cut out one hand along the dotted line and position the lamb so that it is held in this arm. Place the crook in the other hand. Place the sheep on either side.

ot crook into hand.

osition lamb in
he folded arm.

Cut hole
for crook.

Fold under

Cut out hand around dotted line.

Fold under

Fold under

Matthew 25

Glue page on to thin card. Colour and cut out. Make triangular back supports (see following page). Make slits above lamps. Then complete page 23.

THE FIVE WISE GIRLS

Glue page on to thin card.
Colour and cut out.

Set up the five wise
girls at the front
and away behind the
foolish girls. Make
the flames appear in
the wise girls' lamps.

THE FIVE FOOLISH GIRLS

LAMP FLAMES

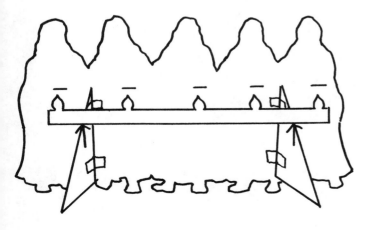

Make triangle back supports and tape
them to backs of figures.
Place flames strip through slots at back
of figures.

Glue page on to thin card. Cut out and colour.
Complete sycamore tree on next page and set
up the scene.

ZACCHAEUS

JESUS AND THE CROWD

Fold back

Glue page on to stiff card. Cut out and colour.
Place Zacchaeus along top branches of the tree
with Jesus and the crowd looking up at him.

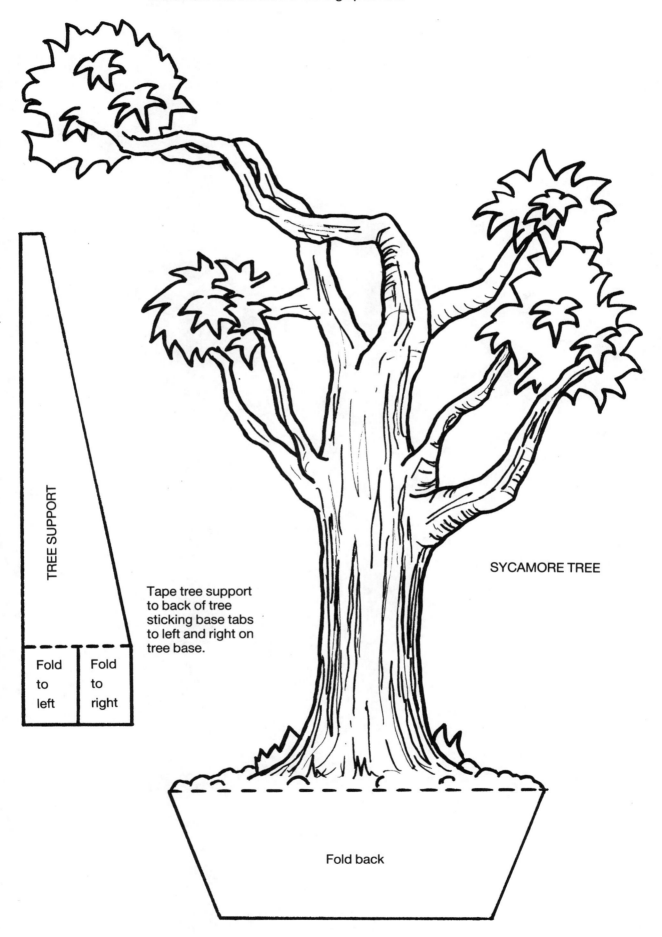

TREE SUPPORT

Fold
to
left

Fold
to
right

Tape tree support
to back of tree
sticking base tabs
to left and right on
tree base.

SYCAMORE TREE

Fold back

Glue page on to thin card. Cut out and colour.
Position figures in front of the arch on following page to make scene.

Fold under

Fold under

Glue page on to card. Cut out and colour. Make back supports if necessary.

Fold under

John 13

After cutting slit in towel, position Jesus so that disciple's heel fits in slit of towel. Place bowl underneath Jesus' hands and jug behind Jesus.

JESUS

CUT SLIT

BOWL

Fold under

Fold under

Fold under

Matthew 26:17-30; Mark 14:12-26 and Luke 22:7-23

Glue all the pieces with a heavy outline on to thin card and colour. Cut them out. Fold under the base of the table and fold the top along the dotted line. Complete the next two pages and set up the finished scene as shown.

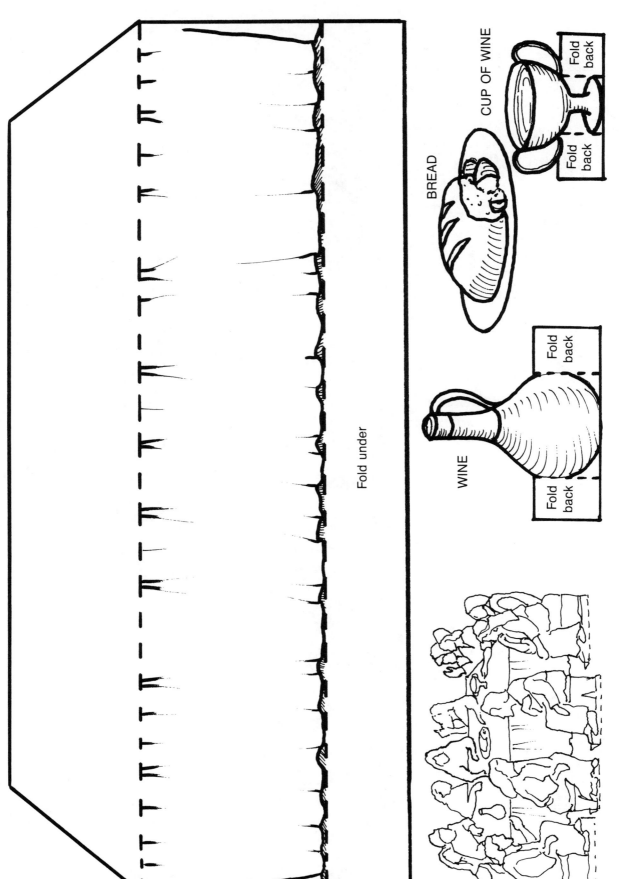

Make three table back supports from card. Cut out a strip of card the same length as the table and about 3cm wide to make a base support. Finish the table as shown. Glue the rest of the page on to thin card and colour. Cut out the figures. For the half-figures, cut round the hands which rest on the table and glue the tabs under the edge of the table.

JESUS

TAB

TAB

TAB

TABLE BACK SUPPORT

BACK VIEW OF TABLE

Fold under

Fold under

The last supper – 3

Glue page on to thin card and colour. Cut out the figures. For the half-figures, cut round the hands which rest on the table and glue the tabs under the edge of the table.

Matthew 26:36-46; Mark 14:32-42 and Luke 22:39-46
Glue page on to thin card and colour. Cut out the figures and arrange them into a scene.

JESUS

Fold under

SLEEPING
DISCIPLES

Fold under

Fold under

Matthew 27:32-44; Mark 15:21-32; Luke 23:26-43

Glue page on to thin card. Colour and cut out.
Cut down dotted line at backs of heads and slot upright
of cross behind the head of Jesus with the hands
over the top. Then Simon of Cyrene carries the upright.

UPRIGHT
OF CROSS

SIMON
OF CYRENE

JESUS

Fold under

Fold under

Matthew 28:9-10; Mark 16:9-11 and John 20:11-18
Glue the figures on to thin card and colour them. Cut them out. Complete the
instructions on the next page and place the figures as shown below.

COMPLETED SCENE

RISEN JESUS

MARY MAGDALENE

Fold under

Fold under

BACK SUPPORT   Tape the back supports to the folded back base.   BACK SUPPORT

Fold under

Jesus appears to two disciples

Mark 16:12-13 and Luke 24:13-35
Glue page on to thin card and colour. Cut out the figures.

JESUS

2 DISCIPLES

Fold under

Fold under

Glue page on to thin card. Colour and cut out.   See page 30.   *Acts 2*

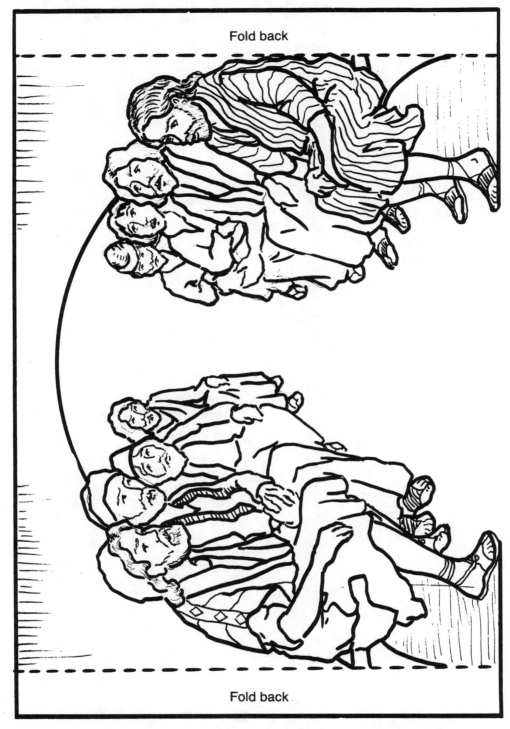

Fold back

Fold back

Glue figures on to thin card.
Colour and cut out.

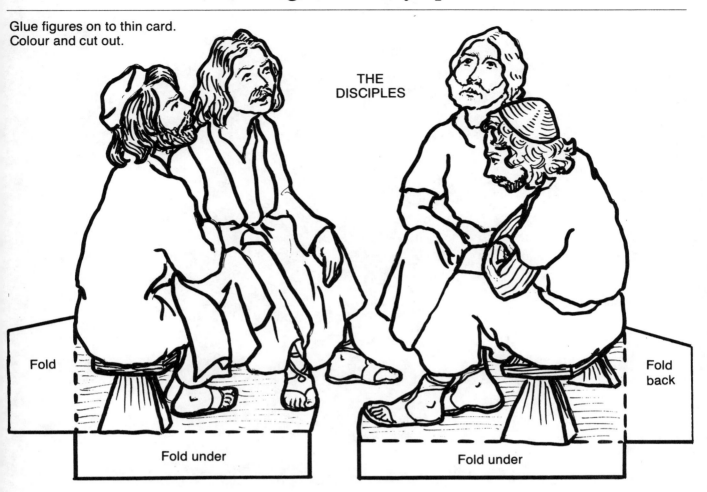

THE
DISCIPLES

Fold

Fold
back

Fold under

Fold under

Using the same building as on page 26, make slit in back wall.
Taping flames together at tabs, slide through slit from back of building
in an upward direction over the disciples' heads.
Set scene up as below.

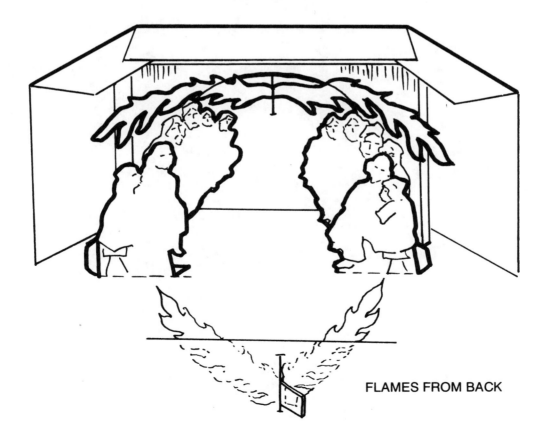

FLAMES FROM BACK